M000048746

What Kids Do...

For information write Andrews McMeel Publishing,
an Andrews McMeel Universal company,
4520 Main Street, Kansas City, Missouri 64111.

www.andrewsmcmeel.com

ISBN: 0-8362-5212-8
Library of Congress Catalog Card Number: 97-80836

98 99 00 01 02 •TWP• 10 9 8 7 6 5 4 3 2 1

Attention Schools and Businesses

Andrews McMeel books are available at quantity discounts
with bulk purchase for educational, business, or sales
promotional use. For information, please write to:
Special Sales Department, Andrews McMeel Publishing,
4520 Main Street, Kansas City, Missouri 64111.

What Kids Do...

Jacques Lowe

A
JACQUES LOWE
VISUAL ARTS PROJECTS
BOOK

**Andrews McMeel
Publishing**

Kansas City

Connect

Improvise

Peek

F*lirt*

Trust

Climb

Cruise

Wonder

Stay cool

Beseech

Balance

Startle

Teach

Dream

Feel

Reflect

Share

Practice

Flutter

Love

Swagger

Harmonize

Grumble

Luxuriate

Dare

Trudge

Lament

Savor

Cuddle

Cherish